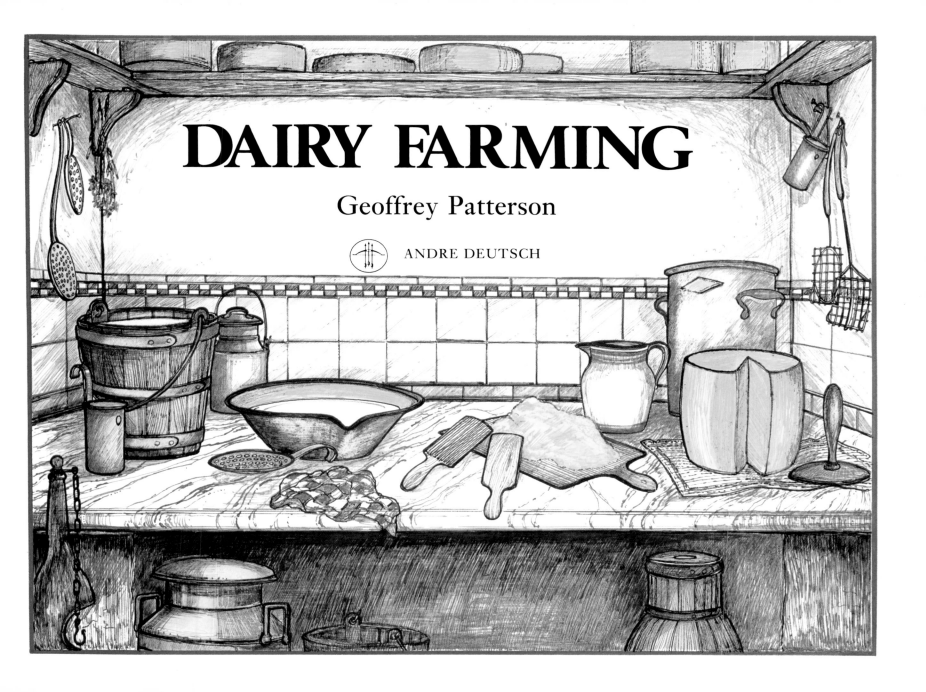

DAIRY FARMING

Geoffrey Patterson

ANDRE DEUTSCH

My grateful thanks are due to Mr. J. R. Shawler and Mr. J. Carter at the Museum of East Anglian Life for their help with technical information about early machinery.

First published in 1983 by
André Deutsch Limited
105-106 Great Russell Street London WC1B 3LJ

Second impression 1985
Third impression 1987

Printed and bound in Belgium by Proost, Turnhout,
Filmset in Ehrhardt by Filmtype Services Limited,
Scarborough, North Yorkshire.

ISBN 0 233 97536 5

Thousands of years ago, in the New Stone Age, the people of Europe and Asia, who had been used to wandering across the land hunting for food, began to settle in small groups and grow crops and rear animals. The wild animals, roaming freely in huge herds, were hard to tame. Gradually, however, people learnt which were the most gentle types and, by breeding from them, slowly developed domesticated animals. Cows were often reared in preference to goats or sheep because they gave more milk.

Celts, Romans, Saxons all brought cows from their own lands with them when they settled in England. However, Highland cattle, with their shaggy, red-coloured coats, still found today in areas where hardiness is important, are thought to be direct descendants of the wild cattle of Stone Age Britain. Another of these early breeds, the little black Dexter cow, is still reared.

These small cows produced enough milk for the small groups of settlers who kept them. Only as the population increased and people began to live in towns, did the farmers who stayed in the country start to breed cows that could produce large quantities of milk for sale in the nearby towns.

After a cow has a calf, or a woman has a baby, she produces a special kind of milk for the first two days. This milk is called 'colostrum' and it contains all the antibodies needed to protect the new-born from infection or disease. Colostrum is rich, yellow milk, and in the old days a farmer would sometimes take a little bit after the calf had finished sucking and make special, delicious little cakes with it. This milk, often nicknamed 'beestings', was highly prized.

Babies and calves are born with the instinct to suck. When a calf sucks at its mother's teat it stimulates the flow of milk into the udder, and the more the calf sucks, so the more milk will the mother cow produce. A calf would naturally live on milk for a few months and then begin to eat grass, sucking less and less milk each day. If left alone, the mother cow would 'dry up' at this stage. But the dairy farmer and his machinery take the place of the calf, and by regular milking he encourages his cow to go on producing more and more milk.

Milk is a marvellous food made up of approximately 87% water, 5% sugar, 4% fat, 3.5% protein as well as 0.5% minerals and vitamins. The percentage of fat and protein varies slightly in the different breeds. Jersey and Guernsey cows, for instance, produce a rich, creamy milk higher in fat content than that of the Friesian, the most popular milking cow.

During the Middle Ages many cottagers kept a cow. If he were lucky, the cottager would own his cow, if not, it would be lent to him by the lord of the manor in return for work. The cottagers grazed their cows on the common land or the village green, and would get from them enough milk to drink and to make butter and cheese. Whey from the cheese-making was used to fatten up the pigs.

Before milking machines were invented cows were milked by hand. The milkmaid milked the cows in the early morning and late afternoon. In the spring and summer she carried her pail and stool out to the cows in the field. She gently squeezed each teat until a stream of warm milk poured out and filled the pail. Although hand-milking was hard work, each cow taking ten minutes or so to milk, it was a pleasant job in fine weather.

In the early years of the eighteenth century, Lord Townsend (nicknamed "Turnip" Townsend) encouraged farmers to grow root crops like turnips for winter feeding when grass was scarce. Up till then shortage of foodstuff had forced farmers to slaughter most of their cattle in the autumn, keeping only one or two for milking and breeding.

1   2   3   4

Early milking pails made of wood with iron hoops (1, 3) were later replaced by all-metal ones (2, 4, 7). The tilted metal bucket (4), has a closed top to keep out the dirt. The metal bucket and seat combined (7) was made at South Marston in Wiltshire, England.

Milking stools (5, 6) usually had three legs to make them steady on uneven ground. They were very strong, with thick elm seats and ash or hazel legs.

5   6   7

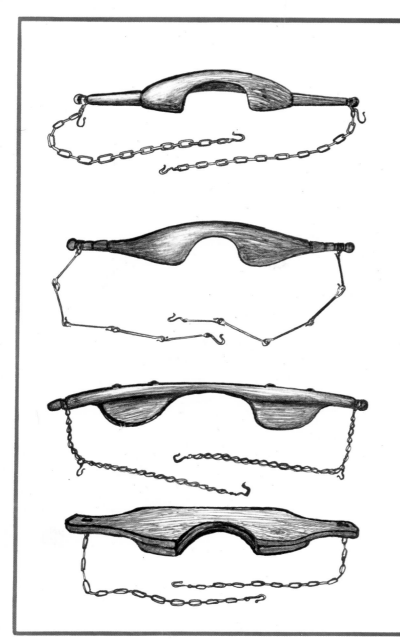

The milkmaid carried the milk to the farmhouse dairy in two pails attached to a shoulder yoke. The yoke was made of light wood, ash or sycamore, and worn across the shoulders. Adjustable chains with hooks supported the heavy pails.

Because they had to be kept cool, dairies were built on the north wall of the farmhouse. Slatted windows provided ventilation and kept out the sun – often a laurel tree would be planted outside the window to give shade. Bench tops covered with slate or stone also helped keep the milk cool.

To make butter, fresh milk was poured into a glazed earthenware or tin setting dish and left overnight. By morning the cream would have separated from the milk, so could be skimmed off the top with a "fleeter" and put into a butter churn. European farmers sometimes used scallop shells as fleeters, but they were difficult to handle and never became popular.

Many different kinds of churns for making butter were designed. The dairymaid first filled the iron-bound, wooden "plunger churn" pictured above with cream, then moved the perforated plunger rapidly up and down until the cream was beaten into butter.

One of the most popular churns was the "end-over" barrel churn. Cream was poured into one end and the barrel was sealed, then turned end-over-end until the cream thickened into butter. The dairymaid could see how she was getting on through a glass viewing hole in one end of the churn.

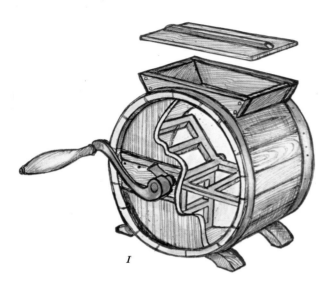

Smaller churns (1, 2) were designed for family use. In the glass churn (2) the handle turned the wooden blades till the cream was stiffened to butter.

After churning, the butter was washed and put on the tray of the "butter worker" (3). The grooved roller went back and forth across the butter, squeezing the water out of it.

Butter beaters or "scotch hands" (4) of alder or sycamore were used to shape the butter. Farmers often pressed a distinctive design onto their butter with a hand carved die or mould before selling it in the market.

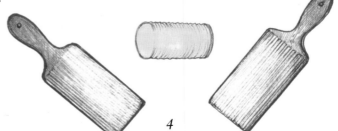

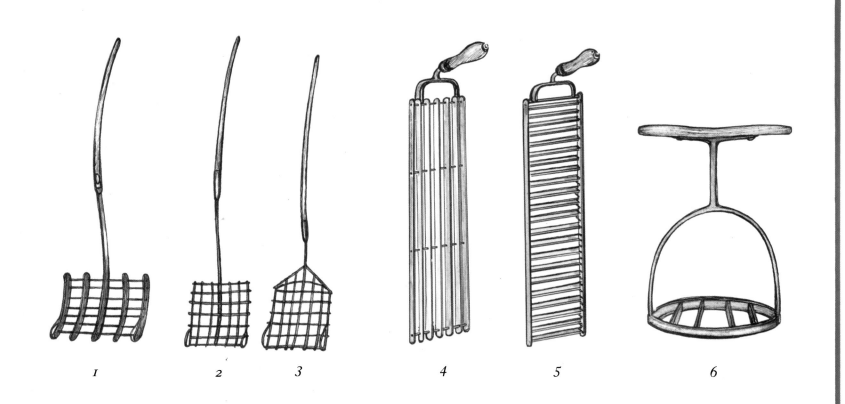

1   2   3   4   5   6

Long ago, so the story goes, milk was carried in bags made from the skin lining of an animal's stomach. A substance contained in the skin, renin, turned the milk into a soft solid – so the first "cheese" was made. Later the dairymaid added renin (rennet), to warmed milk and stirred the mixture with a "curd agitator" until it coagulated and thickened. Curd agitators (1, 2,

3) were made by fixing a square of wire mesh to a beech wood handle. The thickened curd, or junket, was cut into cubes by pushing "curd knives" (4, 5, 6) through it.

Making cheese was a good way of using spare milk. It kept for months and could be eaten in winter when the cows were dry and there was no fresh milk.

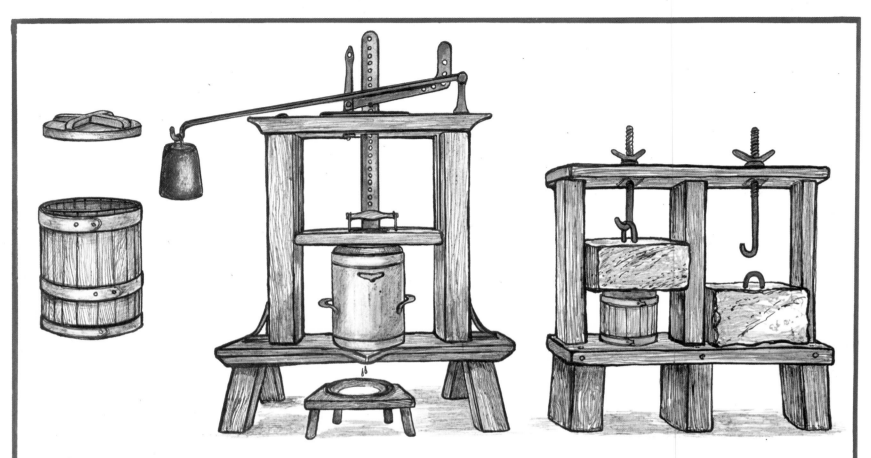

When the cubes of junket were heated the whey separated out and was fed to the pigs. The curds were made into cheese.

First they were salted, then wrapped in muslin and placed in a mould called a "chesset". A round wooden block known as a "follower" was put on top and a weight pressing on the follower squeezed out any remaining whey. On some of the early presses stones were used as weights.

When the cheeses were completely free of whey they were removed from the chessets and put aside to mature. They were turned daily to make sure they ripened evenly and never went mouldy. The dairymaid was proud of her skill, and would never have had it said that her cheese was only fit for the mice.

In the nineteenth century the Industrial Revolution sent more and more people into rapidly growing towns in search of work in factories.

In some towns an area of open land called "town land" was preserved where a few people managed to graze cows. They took their cows into the streets or markets, milked them there, and sold the fresh milk to the factory workers for their families.

Milk did not stay fresh very long, even in cold weather, so it had to reach the towns quickly to be of any use. One way of getting it to them was by donkey. They could manage the rough tracks, and were ridden by "milk boys", with the churns strapped to the side of the donkey.

A TOWN DAIRY IN GOLDEN LANE, LONDON

The problem of getting fresh milk in towns was so great that some people kept cows in sheds and back yards. These "town dairies" often provided miserable conditions for the cows and were, moreover, very dirty. Hay was brought in from the country, and the cows were also fed on brewers' grain. They were milked where they stood, and the milk, butter and cheese were sold over a counter in front of the yard. Such conditions were bound to bring disease. In the 1860s there were several cattle plagues. A particularly bad one in 1865 destroyed all but 375 of the 9,531 kept in London.

The building of railways meant that at last the farmer could rely on getting milk, carried in churns, to the town before it went sour.

In 1866 George Barham became the first man to start a dairy company in London, selling milk brought by rail from farms in the Home Counties. Within two years he was bringing four million gallons a year to the city, and town dairies gradually disappeared.

His milk was carried from door to door on horse-drawn floats or ....

... hand-pulled "perambulators".
The milk was carried in a fifty gallon churn, and measured in ladles. Regular customers soon brought along measured jugs of their own.

By the 1880s George Barham and others had started selling milk in bottles. This not only saved time, but, since the bottles were covered, kept the milk free from germs.

In the country farmers improved their cowsheds to meet the demand. Clean, efficient milking parlours like this one were designed, and a real interest in breeding good dairy cows developed. George III, or "Farmer" George, had helped to found the Board of Agriculture at the end of the eighteenth century, and now the board was ready with advice.

Milk, though a fine food, was also a carrier of germs. If, for instance, people drank milk from a cow infected with TB, the disease could be transmitted to them through the milk.

It was in 1860 that Louis Pasteur, the great French scientist, discovered he could destroy unwanted microbes in wine by heating it at a temperature of 55°C for several minutes. He experimented with milk, and found that the microbes were destroyed at the same level of heat. At last a way had been found to make milk as safe as it was nourishing.

Through the centuries many different vessels have been used for carrying milk. The earliest were skin bags. Hundreds of years later milk was carried down from high pastures in back packs, but they were metal, and held as much as seven gallons; the railways, in their turn, used ten gallon churns.

In 1884 the first successful milk bottle was designed, with a glass stopper that closed against a rubber ring. Also in the 1880s a wide necked bottle was introduced, with a cardboard disc that fitted the rim. Nowadays bottles have foil caps, and milk is also often sold in waxed cartons.

As late as 1950 some cows were still hand-milked, although in 1841 an American named Colvin had designed a milking machine that worked on the vacuum principle. Unfortunately its unbroken sucking action damaged the cows' teats, causing them to bleed, so the machine had to be abandoned. Many others followed it, but they were all either unhygienic or inefficient.

Then in 1895 a Dr Shields from Glasgow invented a machine which pulsated regularly every few seconds, sucking in just the same way as a calf. The principle adopted in the design of this machine is still used in today's sophisticated machinery.

The four teat cups are first slipped over the cow's teats and then air is pumped through the airline so that it squeezes the soft rubber linings of the cups together. The air is then sucked out again, pulling the rubber linings and creating a vacuum.

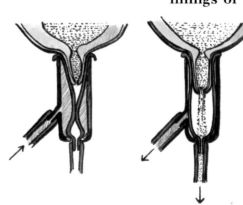

The amount of milk given by dairy cows varies from breed to breed. One of the best, for example, is the Friesian which can yield as much as 95,500 litres or 167,125 pints in a lifetime. That is the equivalent of about 12.78 litres or 22½ pints every day of her milking life.

Five breeds of milking cow often found on dairy farms in Holland.

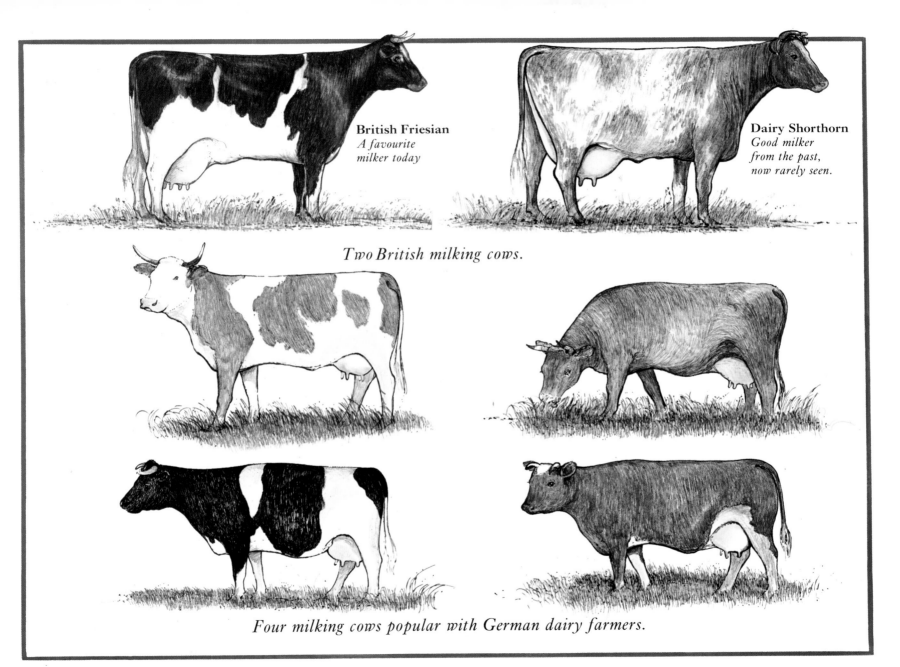

British Friesian
*A favourite
milker today*

Dairy Shorthorn
*Good milker
from the past,
now rarely seen.*

Two British milking cows.

Four milking cows popular with German dairy farmers.

Milking machines and parlours have come
a long way since Dr Shield's first machine in 1895.
In a "rotary" parlour, one of the latest developments,
one man can milk a hundred and twenty cows in an
hour. Each cow in the herd has a number, and the size
of her feed is regulated by the amount of milk she
gives. When being milked, the cows step onto a slowly
revolving ramp. Their udders are washed and dried
automatically before the cowman fits the teat cups. It
takes from six minutes to milk a cow.

The milk is pumped direct from the milking parlour into refrigerated stainless steel "Vats" or tanks. These tanks hold two or three hundred gallons of milk, which is cooled in them to 4.5°C.

Milk is no longer collected in churns. Instead the Milk Marketing Board's insulated tankers go from farm to farm collecting the milk and delivering it to the bottling plant.

Today's bottling plants are fully automated factories. When the milk arrives it is pasteurised by heating to 63°-66°C, for half an hour, then bottled at high speed. At some plants a quarter of a million pints are bottled in a day.

Different quality milk is identified by the colour of the cap put on the bottle. The richest milk, from Channel Islands cows, has a gold top, ordinary milk, which most of us drink, has a silver top.

INDEX